£1-20

THE NORMANS ARE COMING!

FOR MOTHER

First published 1987 by
MACMILLAN CHILDREN'S BOOKS
A division of Macmillan Publishers Limited
London and Basingstoke
Associated companies throughout the world

Picturemac edition published 1990

Reprinted 1991

ISBN 0–333–51610–9

A CIP catalogue record for this book is
available from the British Library

Printed in Hong Kong

THE NORMANS ARE COMING!

THE TRUTH ABOUT 1066

MACMILLAN CHILDREN'S BOOKS

M

GILLIAN CLEMENTS

The Bayeux Tapestry

This famous 230-foot tapestry tells in words and pictures the story of the invasion and conquest of England by the Normans of northern France in the year 1066, over 900 years ago.

When the old King of England, Edward the Confessor, died in 1066, Harold, Earl of Wessex, seized the throne, even though he had already sworn to be faithful to the rightful heir, William, Duke of Normandy.

William was quick to take his revenge. He set sail across the Channel with his soldiers, horses and their provisions, and landed near Hastings in Sussex.

At that time King Harold and his army were fighting against invaders from Norway in the north of England, so the Normans had no difficulty in capturing Hastings and setting up their camp. Duke William knew that Harold would soon hear of the invasion and he sent scouts to watch for the English army.

The English came and, although they were tired and hungry after their long march from the north, at first it seemed they would win the battle. But when they broke ranks to chase the Normans they were surrounded. Harold was killed and his army defeated.

Duke William – known as William the Conqueror – became King of England and the rule of the Norman French began. Soon afterwards work was started on the great tapestry: it can still be seen in the town of Bayeux in northern France.

Our story begins at a school, not far from Hastings.

DUKE WILLIAM'S ARMY WAS APPROACHING ENGLAND

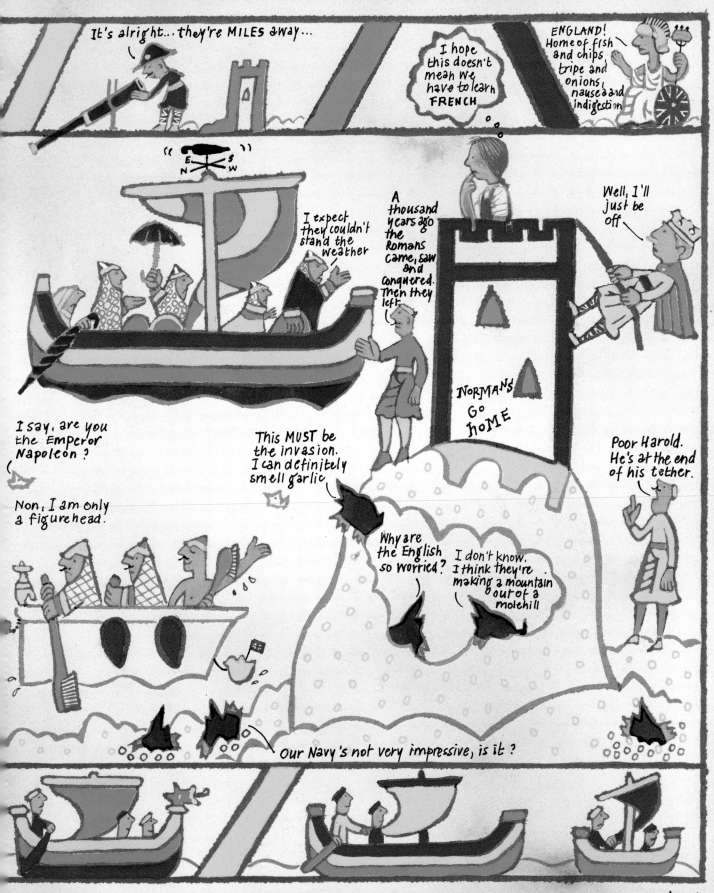

EACHED ENGLAND AT PEVENSEY NEAR HASTINGS:

AS THE FRENCHMEN LAY IN WAIT FOR HAROLD'S RETURN,

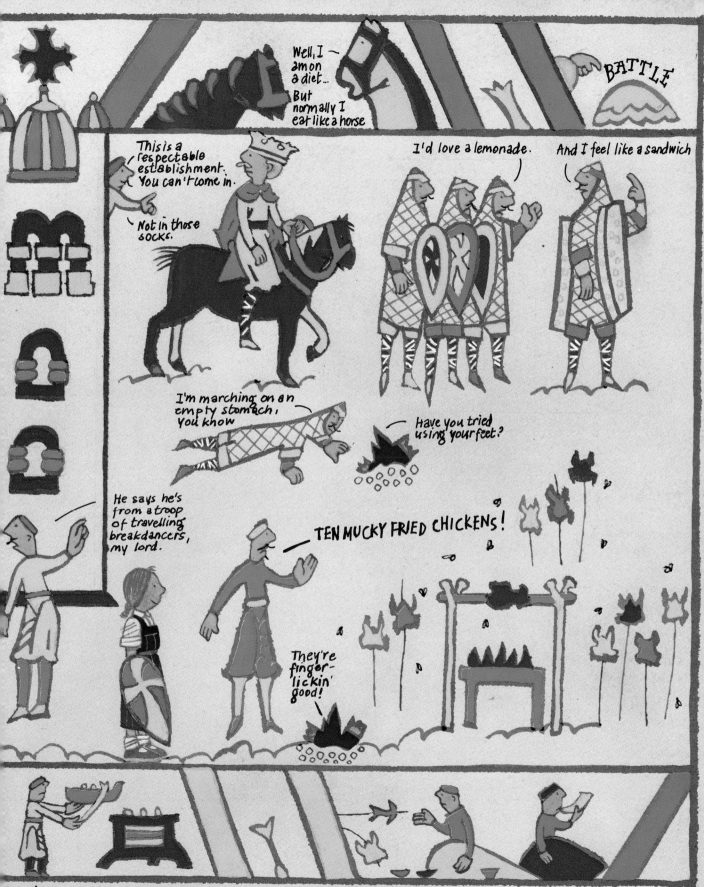

HEY ENTERED HASTINGS AND HAD A GREAT FEAST:

BEFORE THE BATTLE, SCOUTS GATHERED

AT FIRST THE ENGLISH ARMY HELD THE HIGHER

ROUND : BUT ITS DISCIPLINE WAS VERY BAD :

THE FRENCHMEN WERE WELL-ARMED,

IND THREATENED THE ENGLISH WITH DEFEAT:

Other Picturemacs you will enjoy:

BRINGING THE RAIN TO KAPITI PLAIN Verna Aardema/Beatriz Vidal
THE WILD SWANS H C Andersen/Amy Ehrlich/Susan Jeffers
TIM'S LAST VOYAGE Edward Ardizzone
GHOST'S HOUR, SPOOK'S HOUR Eve Bunting
A FIRST TREASURY OF NURSERY RHYMES Michael Foss
AESOP'S FABLES Heidi Holder
HIAWATHA H W Longfellow/Susan Jeffers
TEN CATS AND THEIR TALES Martin Leman
A SCHOOL BEWITCHED E Nesbit/Naomi Lewis/Errol Le Cain
HENRY'S QUEST Graham Oakley
HETTY AND HARRIET Graham Oakley
HENRIETTA GOOSE Abigail Pizer
MISS FANSHAWE AND THE GREAT DRAGON ADVENTURE Sue Scullard

For a complete list of Picturemac titles write to:

Macmillan Children's Books,
18–21 Cavaye Place, London SW10 9PG